BEAU PEEP

BY ROGER KETTLE & ANDREW CHRISTINE

SERGEANT BIDET

DENNIS

DORIS

THE NOMAD

COLONEL ESCARGOT

EGON

SOPWITH

MAD PIERRE

©1985 Express Newspapers PLC, Fleet St., London, EC4P 4JT

AN EXPRESS BOOKS PUBLICATION

Printed by Eyre & Spottiswoode, Cosham, Hants. & co-ordinated by Roeder Print Services Ltd.

As this is my sixth book, I thought it was time to explain how my two chroniclers set about their business. To capture the flavour of my life in the legion, months of research are needed. To make my visits to the pub authentic, the lads (Roger Kettle, writer and Andrew Christine, artist) forced

themselves to spend hours at a time in hundreds of bars throughout the country. "It was a terrible sacrifice," said Roger, "but one we felt necessary!" Andrew agreed. "It was hell. Sometimes after hours of research, we could hardly stand." To learn about the desert, Roger looked at a postcard of Morocco. Enough about them. Come on in ...

THE ADVENTURES OF LEGIONNAIRE
BEAU PEEP

FROM THE STAR

NORTH IS THIS WAY... NO, THIS WAY... NO, OVER HERE....

THIS COMPASS IS GOING CRAZY! IT'S SPINNING ROUND!

THAT'S MY STOPWATCH.

ALL THE GREAT WRITERS HAVE SPENT SOME TIME IN PRISON.

12/3

IN FACT THE OPENING WORDS OF A CLASSIC BOOK ARE PROBABLY WRITTEN ON A WALL IN THIS CELL!

WHY, I DON'T BELIEVE IT! THERE'S SOMETHING WRITTEN HERE UNDER THE DUST!

"THERE WAS A YOUNG LADY FROM MALTA..."

I'VE KEPT A DIARY OF MY HELL IN PRISON!

1214

I'LL PUBLISH IT! I'LL EXPOSE THE HORRORS OF THE SYSTEM!

THEY'LL TRY TO STOP ME BUT I'LL BE FEARLESS I WILL NEVER GIVE IN!

CLICK!

WHAT'S THAT?

NOTHING!

1253

1254

GERONIMO!

LEAP!

1259

WHAT IS IT, BEAU?

IT'S A HUGE BIRD CIRCLING GRACEFULLY IN THE SKY — LOOKS LIKE A GIANT VULTURE.

IT *IS* A GIANT VULTURE. IT'S CIRCLING OVER THAT BERK WITH THE WINGS.

I WANT YOU TO REPORT FOR DUTY AT 0600 HOURS.

1260

RIGHT, SARGE! NO PROBLEM! 0600, IT IS! I'LL BE THERE!

QUESTION IS, WHERE WILL THE BIG HAND BE?

WHEN THE BIG HAND POINTS UPWARDS, DENNIS, IT'S SOMETHING O'CLOCK.

1263

AND WHEN THE —

JUST A MINUTE.

YOU'RE STUPID! IT WAS POINTING UPWARDS THERE BUT WHEN IT'S ON YOUR WRIST IT ONLY POINTS SIDEWAYS!

EXCEPT WHEN YOU'RE ON YOUR HEAD... WAIT... NO! IT STILL GOES SIDEWAYS!

TRY AGAIN, DENNIS, WHAT TIME IS IT?

IT'S...IT'S...

I'LL TELL YOU! IT'S TIME WE PACKED IN THIS STUPID THING AND WENT TO THE PUB!

1264

CLOSE ENOUGH, YOUR ROUND, I BELIEVE.

LOOK WHO IT IS!

IT'S THE COLONEL'S DAUGHTER!

I HOPE YOU'RE NOT GOING TO BEHAVE LIKE A LOVESICK SCHOOLBOY THIS TIME, DENNIS.

CATCH ME!

1295

APPARENTLY, THE COLONEL'S DAUGHTER IS STAYING AT THE FORT ALL WEEK.

1296

SO IF YOU BUMP INTO HER, JUST BE POLITE AND CALM.

OKAY.

HELLO. YOU'RE DENNIS, AREN'T YOU?

HELP ME, BEAU!

WHAT DO WE DO WHEN THE ODDS ARE AGAINST US, MEN?

WE SING A ROUSING LEGION SONG TO RAISE OUR SPIRITS!

WHAT DO WE *NOT* DO?

SING "DE CAMPDOWN LADIES."

JUST GIVE ME A PIECE OF TOAST— EVEN YOU CAN'T RUIN THAT.

DAMN! THE TOAST'S BOILED OVER!

THE GREAT ASTRO IS HERE!

HE IS ALL-SEEING, AND ALL-KNOWING!

WOULD THAT I HAD HIS GIFT! THE COSMOS HOLDS NO SECRETS FOR ASTRO!

COULD SOMEBODY HELP ME? I CAN'T FIND THE FLAP.

...SO, I WANT YOU TO KEEP YOUR NOSE TO THE GROUND.

DO YOU MEAN "EAR," SIR?

NO, I MEAN OUTSIDE! HAR-DE-HAR!

NEXT!

1409

1410

SERGEANT'S EXAM:—
Q) HOW WOULD YOU
TEST A SHAKY
SWING-BRIDGE?

1307

I'd order one of
the men across
first.

Incidentally, it's
stuff like this that
really makes me
want to be a
sergeant.

SERGEANT'S EXAM:—
YOUR MEN ARE
EXHAUSTED. HOW
WOULD YOU COAX
FURTHER EFFORT?

1308

Bullying.
I'd Bully
non-stop.

Bully, Bully,
Bully!

HAND ME THOSE
STRIPES, BABY!

YOU WANT TO GET RID OF BEAU PEEP, RIGHT?

RIGHT!

HONEST ABDUL

13/1

IF YOU'LL FORGIVE ME, I FEEL YOU'VE BEEN A TRIFLE BASIC UP TO NOW.

WHY NOT TRY THIS SUBTLE SLEEPING-POWDER? APPROACH THE PROBLEM WITH CUNNING. IT'S—

A BASEBALL BAT! I'LL TAKE IT!

LEAP

DUL

I CAN FEEL IT NOW!

SWISH!

13/2

THAT SATISFYING CLUNK WHEN I BOP OL' FOUREYES!

SWISH!

BUT WAIT—IS IT RIGHT TO HIT A MAN FROM BEHIND WITH A BASEBALL BAT?

IT MAKES ME LAUGH, ANYWAY.

SWISH!

I SUPPOSE YOU WERE RIGHT, BEAU.

1337

I DON'T THINK I WAS CUT OUT TO BE A TUAREG LEADER...

...BUT I FEEL SORRY FOR THOSE PEOPLE WHO REALLY LIKED AND RESPECTED ME.

LET'S DRINK TO OUR ABSENT FRIEND— EL THICKO!

EL THICKO!

ARE YOU READY?

YES.

REMEMBER, THE IMPORTANT THING IS TO KEEP YOUR HEAD DOWN. GOOD LUCK.

1338

LET'S GO!

HALLOOOOO, CHEEKY-CHOPS!

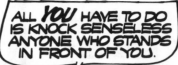

**For further adventures of Legionnaire Beau Peep
get**

every morning

Dear Diary,

The Battle for position continues.

Another Skirmish began around 8a.m. this morning...

...but luckily I escaped injury.

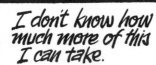

I don't know how much more of this I can take.

I really think the canteen should have two sittings for breakfast.

Dear Lonely Hearts Club,

I would like to meet a nice girl,

She must be blonde, beautiful, good natured and, above all, honest.

Personally, I'm six feet four, slim and rich.

Dear Lonely Hearts Club,

In my first letter, I may have been a bit fussy about my prospective partner.

Tell her not to bother with the photo copy of her bank statement.